Trinity

The International Examinations Board

Guitar

Grade 2

2004–2009

Published by Trinity College *London*
89 Albert Embankment
London
SE1 7TP, UK

Printed in England by Halstan & Co. Ltd, Amersham, Bucks.

Comanche

William Baulch

Moderato ♩ = 72
mf
5
f
pont.
sfz
sfz
9
nat.
mf
f
⑥
⑤
to ⊕ coda
15
mf
19
D.C. al ⊕ coda
⊕ CODA
23
tambor
harm. XII
sfz
perdendosi

O Pulo do Baixo

for Miles Dawson

Jonathan Preiss
(1971–)

Danza Pastorale

arr. Lee Sollory

Antonio Vivaldi
(1678–1741)

New Day

Sveinn Eythorsson
(1964–)

Licence to Chill

Nick Powlesland

Shaken not slurred ♩ = 80
II
legato
mp
mp
5
cresc.
mf
p
9
mp
13
mp cresc.
f
rit.
17
a tempo
mp
20
p
cresc.
23
molto rit.
f
p
pont.

Night Sky

Gary Ryan
(1969–)

Andante ♩ = 72
harm.
XII
XII
VII
harm.
VII
rall.
mp (gentle and calm)
a tempo
VII
V
III
gliss.
rall.
pont.
nat.
(slow arpeggio)
tasto
mf
mp
f
pp

Ejercicio

no. 15 Collection 3a

Jose Ferrer
(1835–1916)

Freestyling

Nick Powlesland

Expressively ♪ = 126
mp
mf
cresc.
f
p
ten.
rit.
a tempo
pp

Etude

op. 44 no. 2

Fernando Sor
(1778–1839)